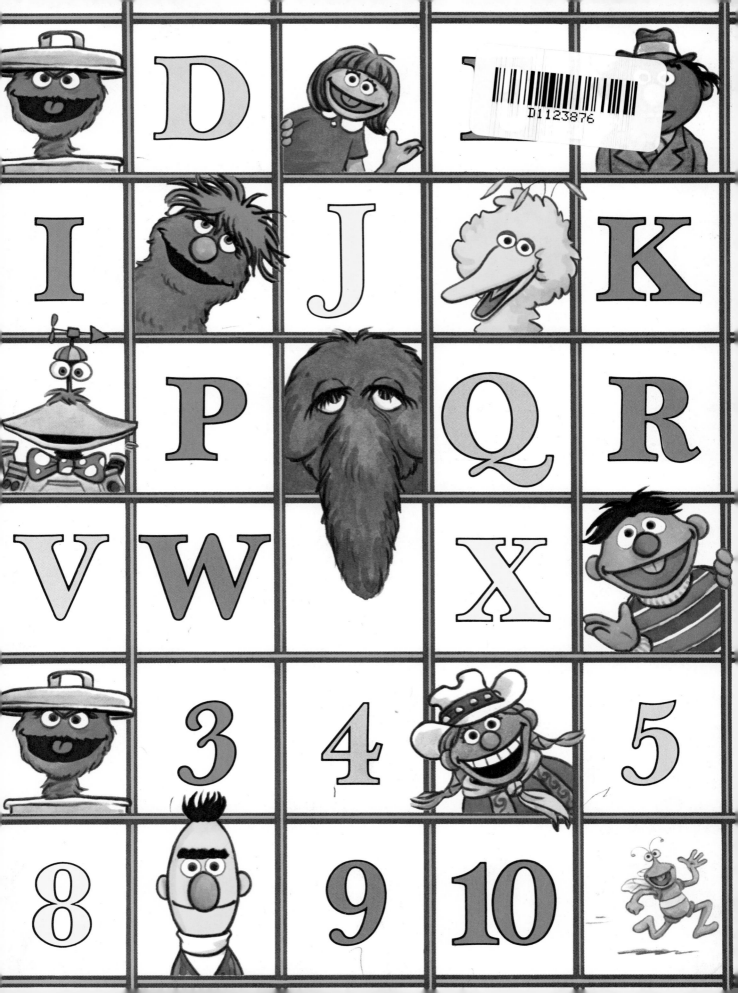

THE SESAME STREET
TREASURY

Featuring Jim Henson's Sesame Street Muppets

VOLUME 13

STARRING
THE NUMBER
13
AND THE LETTER
T

Children's Television Workshop/Funk & Wagnalls, Inc.

WRITTEN BY:

Linda Bove with the
National Theatre of the Deaf

Michael Frith
Jocelyn Gunnar
Emily Perl Kingsley
Sharon Lerner
Jeffrey Moss
Norman Stiles
Pat Tornborg
Ellen Weiss
Daniel Wilcox

ILLUSTRATED BY:

Bill Basso
Tom Cooke
A. Delaney
Robert Dennis
Larry DiFiori
Mary Grace Eubank
Hugh McCarten
Joe Mathieu
Marc Nadel
Michael J. Smollin
Maggie Swanson

PHOTOGRAPHS BY:

Neil Selkirk
View-Master International Group

ISBN: 0-8343-0052-4 (set); 0-8343-0065-6 (vol. 13)

The Thirteenth Thing

A long time ago, at the other end of the world, there was a kingdom called Thirteenia. Around it was a great wall with thirteen gates, and each gate had thirteen locks.

One day Princess Twyla from the nearby kingdom of Twelvia came for a visit with her friend, Princess Thalia of Thirteenia.

Now, Thirteenia didn't get many visitors, and it's easy to see why. Everything, but *everything*, had to be done in thirteens. Sometimes this could get a little tiring.

Breakfast, for instance. When Princess Twyla sat down to eat her first meal in Thirteenia, she was in for a shock.

"Good morning, dear," said the Royal Breakfast-Person. "What'll it be?"

"Oh, just some oatmeal, thanks," said Twyla.

"That's one," said the breakfast-person. "Twelve more to go. You know, you have to order thirteen things for breakfast or we can't bring you any."

"Jeepers," said Twyla. "Okay." She took a deep breath. "Oatmeal, fried eggs, scrambled eggs, ham, grapefruit, milk, toast, er… prunes, anchovies, peanut butter, cheese, and tomato soup." She looked a little green.

"You're almost there," said Princess Thalia. "Just one more."

"Maybe I'll have to skip breakfast." sighed Twyla. "I just can't think of

another thing."

Can *you* think of a thirteenth thing Twyla could order for breakfast?

"Now it's time for our appointment with the Royal Dressmaker," said Thalia after breakfast. "You have to wear a Thirteenia-style dress while you're here, you see." And so off they galloped to the other side of town.

"Hello, dear," said the dressmaker. "What kind of dress would you like?"

"How about a nice blue one?" said Twyla.

"That's one," said the dressmaker. "Just pick twelve more colors and you'll have a snappy dress in no time."

"Oh, brother," sighed Twyla. "I should have known. Okay, here goes: blue,

orange, peach, brown, violet, gray, er... black, gold, white, pink, chartreuse, and mauve."

"Just one more color," said the dressmaker. "You only have twelve, and of course you must have thirteen or I can't make you one at all."

"Maybe we should forget the dress," said Twyla. "I'm getting frustrated."

Can *you* think of a thirteenth color for Princess Twyla's dress?

Just as Twyla was getting used to things, in ran Sir Throckmorton, the bravest knight. "She's back!" he puffed. "She's back!"

"Oh, good grief," said Princess Thalia of Thirteenia.

"What's the matter? Who's back?" asked Twyla.

"It's Throg, the thirteen-headed dragon," said Thalia. "Every once in a while she comes around and asks a question. If we can't answer it, she has a big tantrum and tears up the whole kingdom. And," added Thalia, "she has *very* bad breath."

"What's the question this time?" asked Twyla.

"We have to name thirteen letters of the alphabet," said the knight.

At that moment, in crashed Throg, awful breath coming from each of her thirteen mouths. "Okay!" she roared. "Let's hear those letters!"

"Um... Q," said Throckmorton.

"Let's see," said Thalia. "P, F, H, A, J... boy, it's hard to think with a dragon breathing down your neck."

"I know," said Twyla. "T, X, E, L, W, D!"

"That's only twelve!" roared the dragon. "I can feel a tantrum coming on!"

"I'm too nervous to think of another letter!" gasped Thalia.

Can *you* think of a thirteenth letter to save Thirteenia from the dragon?

"Whew!" said Twyla. "What a day! Thanks for inviting me, but I think I'd like to go home now. In Twelvia we have regular clocks, regular rulers, oatmeal for breakfast, and *no dragons*!"

"Sorry, but you can't go home yet," said Thalia. "Everybody who comes to Thirteenia has to stay for thirteen years!"

"Not I!" said Princess Twyla of Twelvia, and she ran all the way home.

Tubby Time

by Ernie

Tubby time is lots of fun.
It's when I get my scrubbing done!
Rubber Duckie loves the bubbles.
Our sudsy splashing makes big puddles.

After a day of work and play,
I like to float my cares away.
I've rinsed my back and soaped my ears.
I'm squeaky clean as bedtime nears!

The Count's Counting Page

Greetings, my friends! It is I, the Count!
The numbers **1** to **13** are hidden somewhere on these pages.
I want to count them, but I can't find them.
Can you help me?
Find the numbers **1** to **13**.
Now, count the numbers **1** to **13**.

What Is Tickling?

What is tickling?
Tickling is when something touches you very lightly, so that you get an itchy feeling that runs all over you.
What makes this itchy feeling?
Your nerves make this itchy feeling.
What are nerves?
Nerves are things that take messages from your brain to the rest of your body.
Nerves tell you many things.
Nerves tell you if you feel something that tickles you.
Some places that are very tickly are your stomach, the bottoms of your feet, and the backs of your knees.

Grover

Home:	123 Sesame Street
Favorite Food:	Blueberry muffins
Favorite Drink:	Milk
Best Friends:	Everybodee!
Favorite Activity:	Helping
Favorite Color:	Blue
Favorite Flower:	Bluebell
Favorite Clothes:	Cute and adorable blue jeans
Favorite Wish:	To be a good helper
Favorite Sayings:	"Oh, my goodness!"
	"MOMMEEEE!"

When *I* Grow Up
by Big Bird

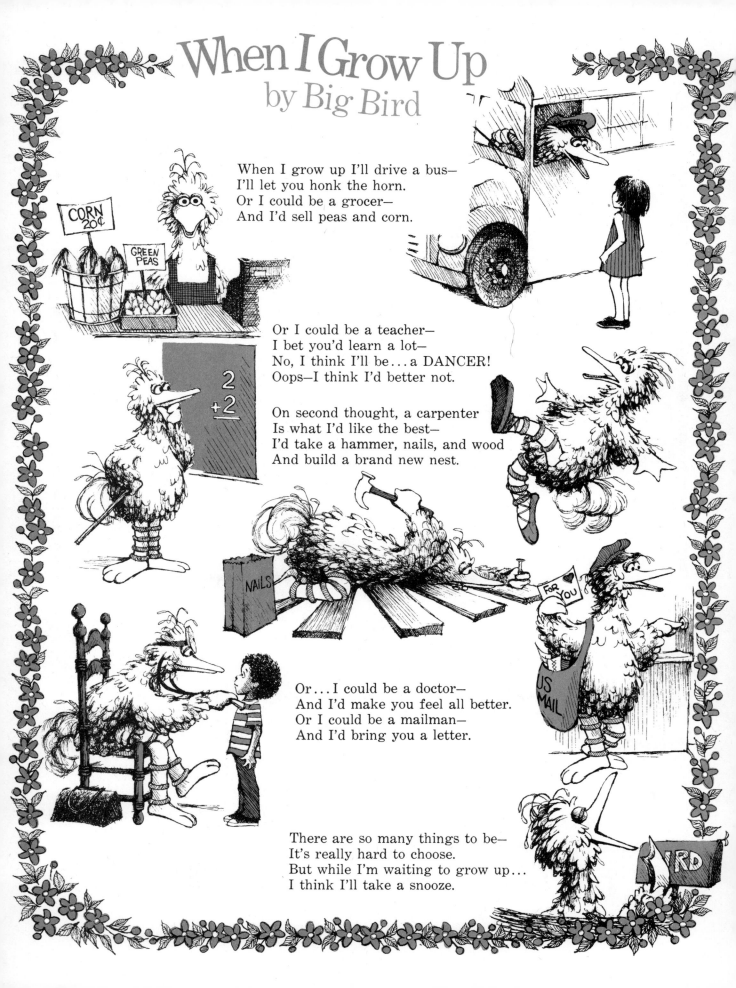

When I grow up I'll drive a bus—
I'll let you honk the horn.
Or I could be a grocer—
And I'd sell peas and corn.

Or I could be a teacher—
I bet you'd learn a lot—
No, I think I'll be...a DANCER!
Oops—I think I'd better not.

On second thought, a carpenter
Is what I'd like the best—
I'd take a hammer, nails, and wood
And build a brand new nest.

Or...I could be a doctor—
And I'd make you feel all better.
Or I could be a mailman—
And I'd bring you a letter.

There are so many things to be—
It's really hard to choose.
But while I'm waiting to grow up...
I think I'll take a snooze.

T t

The Terrible Tickler

*T*he whole town of Tombstone remembers the day
That the Terrible Tickler came riding their way.
He came down the street with a look keen and steady
And said, "Folks, my tickling finger is ready.
Now tickling's terrific and tickling is fun,
And you'll all be tickled before I am done.
For tickling's my pleasure, my greatest of joys.
I think I'll start off with the young girls and boys!"

He first tickled Teddy,
Then Mike, Fran and Sue,
Then Manuel and Mary
And Algernon, too.
Not one could escape,
Though they'd run and they'd wriggle—
Each one would get tickled
And fall down and giggle.
And soon not a boy
Or a girl could be found
Except those who lay
Laughing down on the ground.

"I've got all the kids. Now it's time for the others,"
The Tickler announced. "Next come fathers and mothers."

So the Terrible Tickler
Went on with his work.
He got Nina the plumber
And Charlie the clerk.
He got Sam the barber
And even the mayor
Who fell laughing and giggling
Right out of his chair.

And as sure as five pennies add up to one nickel,
There wasn't one grownup that he didn't tickle.
"I've tickled the people but still I'm not through."
Said the Terrible Tickler, "Now guess what I'll do."

Well, he tickled the horses
And tickled the cows,
He tickled the cats
Till they giggled meows.
He tickled the pigs
And the mules and the dogs.
And he tickled the chickens
And even the frogs.

Then he looked all around and said, "I'm in a pickle.
I'm done and there's nobody left here to tickle.
I've tickled them all now," he said with a frown.
"I guess I'll just have to go find a new town!"
So he tickled a doll sitting high on a shelf.
Then he rode out of town as he tickled—himself.

And everyone said with a giggle and sigh,
"That Terrible Tickler's a mean rotten guy."
And they heard him call back as he giggled with glee,
"Remember that tickle begins with a T."

HOGAR   HOME

Say it in Spanish!

ventana
window

reloj
clock

11 · 12 · 1
10   2
9   3
8 · 7 · 6 · 5 · 4

armario
closet

lámpara
lamp

butaca
armchair

alfombra
rug

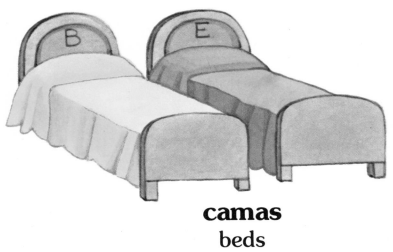

camas
beds

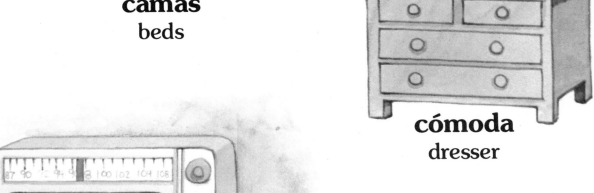

cómoda
dresser

radio
radio

juguetes
toys

cajón de juguetes
toy chest

13!

Presents! Wonderful, wonderful presents! I love to count presents! Count all the presents! How many are there? Whom do you think the presents are for?

basso

The two-headed monster was sitting around one day, just twiddling his thumbs, when he heard a "buzz, buzz." One head picked up his phone, and then the other head picked up his.

"Hello," said the two-headed monster.

"Hi," he replied.

"What do you want?" asked the first head.

"What do you mean?" said the second head.

"Why are you calling?" asked the first head.

"I'm not!" said the second head. "I thought you called me."

"No, no!" said the first head. "You called me."

"I beg your pardon," said the second head, "but you called first."

Then all of a sudden there was another loud "buzz, buzz." The two-headed monster looked at himself and then at the front door. The "buzz" had been the doorbell all along.

The two-headed monster, hanging up the receivers, said, "Gee, I guess we just got our wires crossed!"

transportation

Transportation

car

airplane

train

rocket   motorcycle

bus

truck

helicopter

How many things in this picture can you "sign"?

Do

you

like

to ride

a motorcycle?

TELE-GRAHAMS

What you need:
whole graham crackers
1 package of cream cheese
½ cup of apple butter

What you do:
Leave the cream cheese out of the refrigerator until it is soft. Then spread each cracker with enough cream cheese to cover it smoothly. Put the apple butter in a plastic sandwich bag, and push it into one corner. Cut a small hole in that corner with your scissors. Gather the bag together around the apple butter, and squeeze the apple butter through the hole to write your message on the crackers.

How do birds learn to fly?

A bird learns how to fly when it is a baby—
just as you learned how to walk when you were
a baby.

The baby bird moves around a lot in its nest.
It wriggles and squirms and stretches and
twists. This is how it makes its wings strong.
When its wings are strong, the baby bird can
use them to fly.

When you were a baby, you wriggled and
squirmed and stretched and twisted. That is
how you made your legs strong. When your
legs were strong enough, you used them
to walk.

The mother bird teaches the baby how to fly.
She puts food in her mouth and goes a little
bit away from the nest. She knows the baby
bird wants the food. The baby bird must leave
the nest and fly to get to its mother and
the food.

A baby bird tries over and over again to fly.
Each time it flies, it gets better and better.
Soon it will fly as well as its mother. When you
were little, you tried over and over again to
walk. And now see what you can do!

Betty Lou Lends a Hand

"My, what a blustery, blowy day," said Bert as he stepped out onto Sesame Street. "This is the strongest wind we've had around here in a long time."

Bert held his coat tightly closed against the wind and noticed that all of his friends were out playing touch football in the yard.

"Hey, everybody," called Bert, holding up a small white envelope in his hand. "Come here! I have something to show you!"

Bert's friends stopped their game of touch football and came over to Bert.

"What is it?" asked Ernie.

"Yeah, what've you got there that's so wonderful?" asked Roosevelt Franklin.

"I bet it's a new paper clip for his paper clip collection," Farley whispered to Grover.

"... Or some new pictures of pigeons or something boring like that."

"Oh, it's so fantastic," said Bert, "I can't wait to show you!"

"So let's see it!" said Prairie Dawn. "We interrupted our game of touch football to come over here and see what it is."

Just as Bert was about to open the envelope and show everybody what was in it, a big gust of wind whipped the envelope out of his hand and blew it up into the air.

"Oh, no!" cried Bert. "My

a lot of friends here. I'm sure someone will be able to get the envelope out of there for you."

"Sure, Bert," said Herry. "I'm the *strongest* person here so I'm sure I can get your envelope back for you. And even if there is only a silly, dumb picture of a pigeon inside, I'll help you get it back.

"Now stand back, everybody, and make way for the *strongest* one of all. I will just lift that fence up into

envelope!! The wind is blowing it away! Help!"

The wind carried the envelope high in the air, twisting and turning it, dipping and darting it, sailing it over a big wooden construction fence and onto the ground on the other side.

"Oh, gosh," wailed Bert. "My envelope's behind that big fence. Now what am I going to do?!"

"Gee, Bert," said Ernie. "You have

the air so you can go underneath and grab your envelope. I bet you're glad *I* am here today! Ya!"

Herry grabbed a corner of the fence and pulled up with all his might, but the fence was very firmly planted and he couldn't lift it out of the ground.

"Gee, Herry, thanks a lot," said Bert. "You are very strong, but it looks like strength isn't what we need to get my envelope back."

"Let me try," said Big Bird. "I'm the *biggest*. I'll just reach right over the top of the fence and get your envelope for you. Even if it is just a silly old picture of a pigeon, it's important to you, so I'll help you get it back. Now everybody watch closely as the biggest one here gets the envelope. Here goes. . . ."

Big Bird stood up on tippy-toes and reached as far as he could over the top of the wooden fence, but the fence was too high. Big Bird couldn't reach far enough to get the envelope.

"I'm sorry, Bert," said Big Bird. "I guess bigness is not what you need, either."

"What you need is *smartness*," said Sherlock Hemlock, "and I am the world's smartest detective. I will get that envelope out of there."

"Ahhh," said Bert. "Smartness. Now that's a good idea."

Sherlock Hemlock went over to a skinny little crack in the fence and put his mouth up against it.

"Now, little white envelope on the ground in there, I, Sherlock Hemlock, the world's smartest detective, am talking to you," he said through the crack. "I think you ought to realize how upset you have made our friend Bert by flying over that fence. And even though you probably have nothing but a silly, boring old picture of a pigeon inside you, I think that the *sensible* thing would be for you to come out of there and stop causing Bert so much distress. Now, what do you say?"

Naturally, the envelope just lay there on the ground. Sherlock

"Say, Bert," said the Cookie Monster. "Me the *hungriest.* How about this? Me eat this fence up. Then you can go get envelope. Me not do that for silly, boring picture of pigeon. Me do that because me so hungry and fence look pretty good."

"Oh, Cookie Monster," moaned Bert. "I'm ready to try anything. Eating a fence sounds crazy to me, but if you feel up to it . . ."

Cookie Monster went over to the fence and took a great big, huge bite out of it.

"Blecchhh!" he cried. "That the most terrible fence me ever eat! Boy! Need salt! Need ketchup! Need Worcestershire sauce! No way me can eat whole fence that taste like that! Sorry, Bert. Me want to help but there a limit even to what *me* can eat!"

"*Four* terrible, awful, silly, no-good ideas!" yelled the Count.

"How about *me?*" called Rodeo Rosie. "I'm the *loudest!* You just give

Hemlock threw up his hands. "This silly envelope is *not* responding to logic and reason. I do not understand it."

Bert sighed. "I guess it has no respect for smartness."

"May *I* help?" asked the Count.

"Sure," said Bert. "What do *you* think?"

"I think that you have had three suggestions that did not work. *Three!* You had the strongest, the biggest, and the smartest. That makes three no-good suggestions! Ah-hahahahaha! Happy to be able to help, Bert."

"That didn't help!" snapped Bert.

me a crack at it and I'll have your
silly old pigeon picture back in two
shakes!"

"Go ahead, Rodeo Rosie," shrugged
Bert.

Rodeo Rosie sauntered up to the
fence and put her hands up to her
mouth.

"NOW LISTEN HERE,
ENVELOPE! YOU GIT ON OUTA
THERE RIGHT PRONTO,
Y'HEAR? I GIVE YA A COUNT OF
THREE TO JIST SKEDADDLE

RIGHT ON OUT HERE WHERE
YA B'LONG!! A-ONE, A-TWO,
A-THREE!!" she hollered.

"That certainly was loud," said
Bert, rubbing his ears. "But the
envelope's still sitting there, just like
before. Thanks, Rodeo Rosie, but I
guess loudness wasn't what we
needed either."

Bert gave a deep sigh. "Say, how
about *you*, Betty Lou?" he said.
"You're the only one who hasn't
made a suggestion. Don't you have

any ideas about how to get my
envelope back?"

"Me?" said Betty Lou. "Well, I am
not the biggest or the strongest or
the loudest or the smartest. All I am
is the *smallest*. What could I
possibly do for you?"

"I don't know," said Bert. "But the
biggest and the strongest and the
loudest and the smartest haven't

done much good. I thought you could
come up with something."

"Well, let me look," said Betty
Lou.

She walked up to the skinny little
crack in the fence and looked
through. There was the white
envelope, still lying on the ground.
Betty Lou was about to turn away
when she thought of something.

"Hey," she said. "I'm so small that if I held my hand all flat like this . . . and held my arm out straight like this . . . maybe, just maybe I could just squeeze my little arm right through that crack . . . like this . . . and reach your envelope with my fingers . . . like THIS!!"

And she grabbed the envelope with her fingers and pulled it through the narrow crack in the fence. She held it up high for all to see.

"Hooray for Betty Lou!" everyone shouted.

"Wow," she said. "I did it! I didn't have to be the biggest or the strongest or the smartest or the loudest or anything!! In fact, being the *smallest* was just what you needed! How about that!"

"That's right, Betty Lou," said Bert. "Thank you!"

Bert smiled broadly. "Well, now

that we have the envelope back, wouldn't you all like to see what's in it?"

"Oh, we know what it is, Bert," said Ernie. "Just some silly, boring old picture of a pigeon for your scrapbook. We knew that all along. Probably just a silly old pigeon eating birdseed. . . ."

"Or a pigeon walking on the ground," said Prairie Dawn.

"Or a pigeon sitting on a statue," suggested Herry.

"*I'd* like to see what's in the envelope, Bert," said Betty Lou. "Please?"

"Well, as a matter of fact," said Bert, "it just happens to be . . . tickets to the circus for me . . . and all my friends!"

"Tickets? For the circus? For your friends?" said Ernie, swallowing hard.

"For *all* your friends?" asked Big Bird. "Even the ones who kept teasing you about having a dumb old pigeon picture in there?"

"ALL my friends," shouted Bert, happily. "My strong friends . . . and my big friends . . . and my smart friends . . . and my little friends . . . and my fast friends . . . and my slow friends . . . for *all* my friends!"

"Yaaaay Bert!" cried all his friends.

And they all started out for the circus together.

"And on our way to the circus," said Bert, "I'll tell you all about the great pigeon act we're going to see there. This circus has the *best* trained pigeons! We'll actually see a pigeon stand on one foot. And then we'll see a pigeon who *sits down.* And after that, a pigeon eating a piece of bread. . . . And guess what comes after that?! . . ."

TONGUE TWISTERS

How fast can you say them?

The Twiddlebugs tried
to teach Telly how
to twirl on his toes.

Bert's bottlecaps
bounce better than
Barkley's bone,
but Big Bird's
beach ball bounces
best of all.

Can Cookie cook
more cookies than
the Count can count?

Ernie Talks to the Animals

Can you fill in the blanks
with the correct animal noise?

Ernie was visiting his aunt's farm. It was a beautiful day, so Ernie decided to go outside to play.

The first thing Ernie saw was a pig. "Hi, Pig," said Ernie. "Will you play with me?"

The pig looked at Ernie and said, _____.

"Hmmmm," said Ernie, scratching his head. "Does that mean yes or no?" But the pig didn't answer. It just went on rolling in the mud.

Then Ernie saw a cow. "Hi, Cow," said Ernie. "Will you play with me?" But all the cow said was _____.

"Oh, well," said Ernie. "I guess I'll just ask this horse. Pardon me, Horse, will you play with me?"

But the horse just swished its tail and said _____. So, Ernie asked a sheep. "Say there, nice woolly sheep. Will you play with me?"

What do you think the sheep said? The sheep said _____.

So Ernie asked a rooster. And the rooster said _____.

Then Ernie asked a dog. And the dog said _____.

Then he asked a donkey. And the donkey said _____.

So finally he asked a duck. But the duck said _____.

"Gee," said Ernie. "No one wants to play with me. Not one animal on this farm wants to play. Well, I guess

I'll just stand by this old duck pond until it gets cold and dark because no one wants to play with ol' Ernie."

"I'll play with you," said a voice.

"Who said that?" said Ernie.

"I did," said a girl who was sitting by the pond, fishing. "My name is Nina. I live on the next farm. I've got a ball right here. Want to play catch?"

"Oh boy!" said Ernie. "Do I! You know, I asked all the animals if they wanted to play. But the pig said _____ and the cow said _____ and the horse said _____ and the sheep said _____ and the rooster said _____ and the dog said _____ and the donkey said _____ and the duck said _____. Not one animal said, 'Sure, old buddy Ernie, I'd love to play.'"

"Of course not, silly," said Nina. "Animals don't talk like we do. Pigs go _____ and cows go _____ and horses go _____ and sheep go _____ and roosters go _____ and dogs go _____ and donkeys go _____ and ducks go _____. But that doesn't mean that they don't want to play. Wait and see."

So Ernie and Nina started to play catch. And do you know what happened? First, the pig came and said _____. Then the cow came and said _____. Then the horse came and said _____. Then the sheep came saying _____. Then the rooster came crowing _____. And the dog came barking _____ and the donkey came braying _____. And last, the duck waddled out of the pond and said _____. And the animals sat and watched Ernie and Nina play catch until the sun went down.

TWINKLE, TWINKLE, LITTLE STAR

Twinkle, twinkle, little star,
How I wonder what you are!
Up above the world so high,
Like a diamond in the sky.
Twinkle, twinkle, little star,
How I wonder what you are!